This Little Hippo
book belongs to

Danna

Plain Jack

Written and illustrated by

K M Peyton

Little Hippo

For Rebecca

Scholastic Children's Books
Commonwealth House, 1-19 New Oxford Street,
London WC1A 1NU, UK
a division of Scholastic Ltd
London • New York • Toronto • Sydney • Auckland

First published in Great Britain, 1988
by Hamish Hamilton Children's Books

This edition published by Scholastic Ltd, 1997

Copyright © K M Peyton 1988
This edition copyright © K M Peyton 1997

ISBN 0 590 19546 8

2 4 6 8 10 9 7 5 3 1

Printed in Spain by GZ Printek

The right of K M Peyton to be identified as the author and
illustrator of this work has been asserted by her in accordance
with the Copyright, Designs and Patents Act, 1988.

Once there were two old mares in a field together, who each had a foal.

One mare had won a lot of races and thought a lot of herself. She spoilt her foal dreadfully. She told him how clever he was and what a lot of races he would win when he grew up.

He was very valuable and called Fire of England.

The other mare was very plain and had won
only one small race. Her foal was plain
like her and called Plain Jack.

"You will have to work very hard if you are to be a winner, Plain Jack," she said to him sternly. "You don't come from a family of great winners like Fire."

"All the same," she added tartly, "he'll come to a bad end if he doesn't behave himself."

Jack remembered her words, and when they went to the sales he behaved his very best. But he only fetched a small price. He was bought by a man called Bill who lived in the North.

But Fire, in spite of behaving disgracefully in
the sale-ring, was sold for an enormous price
to a very rich owner, and went to live in the
best stable in England.

"I will try very hard to make Bill pleased with
me," thought Jack.

A lad called Barney looked after him and his jockey was called Joe. They liked Plain Jack because he tried.

When he was ready to race, they took him to Yarmouth. To Jack's surprise he found Fire was entered in the same race.

Fire was ridden by the best jockey in the country.
Everyone admired him. But he was very naughty
and bucked his jockey off. The crowd booed and
someone threw a tomato.

But Plain Jack tried his hardest and came fifth out of twenty-three horses.

Bill and Joe and Barney were very pleased with him.

Every time he ran, Plain Jack tried his hardest, and the crowd liked him because he never let them down.

Barney read to Jack from the racing paper:
"Plain Jack is a great favourite with the racing public."

But on the back page it said: "Fire of England
disappointment." It said Fire was to be sold
because he was no good.

Plain Jack did not see him again until he was sent to run in a race at Epsom.

The racecourse was on the downs, and people were picnicking and playing cricket. Some children were riding along by the rails.

One of the horses was a very thin, poor chestnut. When it saw Plain Jack going down to the start of the race, it put up its head and whinnied. Jack got a great surprise, recognising his old friend Fire.

Jack did not want to race, he wanted to stay with
Fire. When the race started Jack hung back. Joe did
not know what was wrong with him. Fire bucked
his rider off just like old times, jumped the rails
and chased after the race. He ran like the wind.

"Look at that thin old nag!" everyone laughed.
"He's the fastest of the lot!"

But at the end, Fire was caught and led away
in disgrace.

Plain Jack had come last and Bill and Joe and Barney were very disappointed with him.

It was the first bad race he had ever run.

They took him home, but Plain Jack would not eat and stood with his head in the corner thinking of poor Fire.

He got very thin. Bill called the vet, but the vet could find nothing wrong with him.

"I don't understand it," said Bill. "Ever since Epsom . . ."

Barney had an idea. He told Joe to go to Epsom
to try to find out about the thin chestnut horse
who seemed to have upset Jack so.

Joe searched all the riding stables and found Fire
at last, in a grotty shed, with no food or water.
He was thinner than before and very miserable.
  Joe examined him carefully.
  "Why! You're Fire of England – I recognise you!
The day the guv'nor bought Jack, you were sold
for half a million pounds! But you're not worth
tuppence now!"

Joe told Bill and Bill bought Fire from his nasty owner. Joe fetched Fire home.

When he walked in the yard, Plain Jack put his head out of his box and whinnied with excitement.

Bill laughed. "So that was the trouble! Put him in the box next to Jack, and get them each a good feed! I can use Fire for my hack."

Barney brought two big feeds. Both horses ate up every oat – and wanted more!

So Fire of England came back into a racing stable and grew fat and happy again.

Plain Jack went on running races and trying his hardest and never giving in, and the racing public loved him because he never let them down, except that one time.

When Fire and Jack got old and were retired, they were turned out in a field together. They stood under the trees in the shade, swishing their tails –

the horse with a great talent who never used it, and the horse with little talent who used it all.